Mystery Mob
and the Conker Conspiracy

Roger Hurn

Illustrated by
Stik

RISING★STARS

Rising Stars UK Ltd.
22 Grafton Street, London W1S 4EX
www.risingstars-uk.com

The right of Roger Hurn to be identified as the author of this work
has been asserted by him in accordance with the Copyright,
Design and Patents Act 1988.

Published 2008

Cover design: Burville-Riley Partnership
Illustrator: Stik, Bill Greenhead for Illustration Ltd
Text design and typesetting: Andy Wilson
Publisher: Gill Budgell
Editor: Catherine Baker

British Library Cataloguing in Publication Data.
A CIP record for this book is available from the British Library

ISBN: 978-1-84680-428-1

Printed in the UK by CPI Bookmarque, Croydon, CR0 4TD

Contents

Meet the Mystery Mob

Name:

Gummy

FYI: Gummy hasn't got much brain – and even fewer teeth.

Loves: Soup.

Hates: Toffee chews.

Fact: The brightest thing about him is his shirt.

Name:

Lee

FYI: If Lee was any cooler he'd be a cucumber.

Loves: Hip-hop.

Hates: Hopscotch.

Fact: He has his own designer label (which he peeled off a tin).

Name:

FYI: Rob lives in his own world – he's just visiting planet Earth.

Loves: Daydreaming.

Hates: Nightmares.

Fact: Rob always does his homework – he just forgets to write it down.

Name:

Dwayne

FYI: Dwayne is smarter than a tree full of owls.

Loves: Anything complicated.

Hates: Join-the-dots books.

Fact: If he was any brighter you could use him as a floodlight at football matches.

Name:

Chet

FYI: Chet is as brave as a lion with steel jaws.

Loves: Having adventures.

Hates: Knitting.

Fact: He's as tough as the chicken his granny cooks for his tea.

Name:

Adi

FYI: Adi is as happy as a football fan with tickets to the big match.

Loves: Telling jokes.

Hates: Moaning minnies.

Fact: He knows more jokes than a jumbo joke book.

He Stoops to Conker

The Mystery Mob are in the park.
They are looking for conkers under
the trees.

A National Conker Competition is taking
place in their town. The winner gets
a crown made of conkers and a big
cash prize. The Mob all want to enter –
and Adi reckons he can win.

Adi   I'm bonkers about conkers.

Chet   No, Adi. You're just bonkers.

Adi   Maybe, but I'm going to win the conker crown.

Chet   You're a great conker player, Adi, but Billy Basher will beat you.

Adi   (crossly) How do you know?

Chet   'Cos he's a real hard nut!

Adi   Doh! I make the jokes around here, Chet.

Chet   Okay, but Billy Basher is
the champ and he hates to lose.
If you beat him, he won't think
you're funny. He'll turn nasty,
and then the joke will be on you.

Adi   Billy Basher doesn't worry me.
I'll beat him fair and square.

Chet   Well, you can try.

Adi   All I need is a killer conker.

Chet   If you say so.

Adi   I do say so, and I think
I've just found exactly
what I'm looking for.

Adi holds up a big brown shiny conker.
The Mystery Mob gather round and stare
at it in wonder.

Chet   Wow, that's a stonker of a conker!

Adi (chanting) It's a smasher and
a masher – it'll fix Billy Basher!
His conker won't stand a chance.
The conker crown is as good
as mine.

The boys all look at each other.
They know Billy Basher. He's
the conker king. He never loses.

Chet In your dreams, Adi.

11

The Conkering Hero

Dwayne has given Adi a book called
How to Conquer with your Conker!. Adi has
his nose in it when Chet comes to see him.

Chet   Hey, Adi, are you coming out
             for a game of football?

Adi   No way, Chet.

Chet   Why?

Adi   I've got to read this book
             on how to win at conkers.

Chet   Okay. What does it say?
Have you picked up any top tips?

Adi   You bet I have. Listen to this.
The secret of turning a weedy
little conker into a winner
is to soak it in vinegar for a week,
then bake it in an oven.
That makes it really hard.
So that's what I'm going to do.

Chet   Brilliant. But there's only
one problem.

Adi   What's that?

Chet   The conker competition
is tomorrow.

Adi   Doh!

Chet   Yeah, but there's no need to panic. Your conker isn't weedy. It's as hard as Gummy's head.

Adi   True.

Chet   And anyway, it's only cheats who do that stuff to their conkers.

Adi   Hmmm. I guess so.

Chet   Oh come on, Adi. You're not a cheat and you never will be.

Adi   But don't they say that nice guys never win?

Chet   I didn't say you were a nice guy.
          I said you weren't a cheat.

Adi   Thanks, Chet. You're a real mate.
          But if I'm going to win without
          cheating, you've got to help me.

Chet   You've got it. What do you want
          me to do?

Adi   I need to work on my
          conker-hitting skills.

Chet   So how can
          I help?

Adi   All you've got to do is dangle
this conker on a bit of string
while I whack it with 'Killer'.

Chet   Who's 'Killer'?

Adi   My super-hard conker of course.

Adi gives Chet a piece of string with a tiny
conker hanging on the end of it. Chet
holds the string while Adi takes aim.

Chet   Just you be careful with that thing, Adi.

Adi   I'll be fine. Now keep still. Right, here we go. Fire!

Adi lets fly with the huge conker. He misses his target, but he does hit something.

Chet   Argggghhhh! You've hit me on the fingers!

Chet sticks his hand in his armpit
and groans. Adi checks out his conker.

Adi   Oh, don't be such a wuss. At least
            'Killer' is still in one piece.
            Now get ready – I'm having
            another go.

Chet   No way. I don't want to end up
            in hospital.

Adi   Chet, you are such a wimp ...
            Wait a minute. I've had a
            brainwave!

Adi dashes off into
the kitchen. He comes
back clutching a large
oven glove.

Chet   What now? Are you going to bake
your conker after all?

Adi   No! Just put this thick glove on.
Then, even if I miss with Killer,
you won't be hurt.

Chet   Adi, why couldn't you have come
up with this idea before we
started?

Adi   You're never happy, are you,
Chet? Now, hush up and let's
have some conker action!

The All-conkering Conker

It's the day of the conker competition.
The Mystery Mob are ready to rumble.

Chet   Hey, Lee's first up. Come on Lee.
Do your stuff.

Adi   Oh no. Lee's dropped his conker
... and now he's trodden on it.
He's out!

Chet   Never mind. Gummy's next. Maybe he'll do better.

Adi   Oh no! I don't believe it. Gummy's got a sweet chestnut on the end of his string – not a conker.

Chet   Hang on. He's not fighting with it. He's eating it – and the string! Yuk, that's just soooo gross!

Adi   Oh, forget Gummy. It's Rob's turn now. I bet he'll be good.

Chet   Maybe, but football's Rob's game – not conkers.

Adi   You're right. Look, he's playing keepie-uppie with his conker.

Chet   Oi, Rob. You're meant to hit it, not kick it!

Adi   Yeah, and now the ref has kicked him out of the competition.

The ref calls Chet and Dwayne over. They have to play each other. Both their conkers shatter on the first hit, so they knock each other out.

Now it's Adi's turn. He does well
in his first game, and then he wins
the second too. He wins game
after game, until there's only
one game left ...

Chet   Wow, Adi, you're ace at this.
I never thought
you'd make it
to the final!

Adi   Cheers, Chet –
but I proved
you wrong,
didn't I?

Chet dashes off
to find out who
Adi's playing in the final. When he
comes back, he does not have good news.

Chet   Hard luck, Adi. You're playing
             Billy Basher!

Adi   So?

Chet   Billy's awesome. He's winning
             all his games with one hit.

Adi   What?!

Chet   Yeah, it's amazing. I reckon
             he's got the hardest conker
             in the world.

Adi   Is it as big as Killer?

Chet   No, it's quite small. But I don't rate Killer's chances. Billy's conker is the Master of Disaster.

Adi   Hmmm. I think I need to go and see it for myself.

Chet   Why? The ref checks the conkers before each match. So that conker's cool.

Adi   Yeah? So why have I got a funny feeling about it?

Going Conkers

Adi and Chet push through the crowd to get to Billy. He has a sly look on his face. Before they can reach him he slips away.

Chet   He's up to something.
              Quick, let's follow him.

Adi   Right. Maybe we'll find out
              the secret of his success.

The boys go after Billy. Something drops out of Billy's back pocket.

Chet   Hey, what's this?

Adi   It's his super conker.

Chet   Well, we'd better give it back
to him.

Adi   No, wait a sec.
He's also dropped this.

Chet   What?

Adi   It's a tube of 'Tuff Enuff
See-Thru Glue'. Billy's painted
his conker with it. No wonder
it can't be beaten. He must be
sneaking off to give it a fresh coat
before the final.

Chet   The cheat! Let's go and tell the ref.

Adi   No, I've got a better idea.

Adi pulls a ping-pong ball, a magic marker multicolour pen, a safety pin and a box of stink bombs out of his pocket.

Chet   Adi, I know you're a joker, but what are you doing with all that stuff?

Adi   Watch and learn.

The ping-pong ball is the same size
and shape as Billy's conker.
Adi makes a tiny hole in it
and fills the ball with pong from
the stink bombs. Next Adi seals
the hole with a dab of see-thru glue.
Then he colours the ball brown
and fixes the string to it.

Chet   Wow. It looks exactly the same
as the super conker!

Adi   It sure does. Now let's find out
            where Billy went.

The boys hear voices coming from
the ref's room. It's Billy and the ref.
They're hatching a plot.

Chet   I can't believe my ears!
            The ref knows Billy's a cheat –
            and he's in on it with him!

Adi   I knew it! They're going to fix
            the final and split the prize money.

Chet   Cheats! But how can we
stop them?

Adi   That's easy! We'll leave the fake
conker outside the ref's room.
Billy will find it when he comes
out. He'll think it's the one
he dropped. He'll never know
it's been nobbled!

The boys hear a howl of fury from inside
the room.

Adi   Whoops! It sounds like Billy's just found out he's lost his winning conker.

Chet   Right. Leg it!

Adi and Chet run off. Billy storms out of the ref's room. Then he sees the fake conker on the floor. He grins and picks it up.

Billy   Yesss! Bring it on. Now I've got my conker back for the final, I can't lose!

Billy Conks Out

It's the final of the conker competition.
A big crowd is waiting to see Adi play
Billy Basher. Nobody thinks Adi has
a chance of winning.

Adi   I've got butterflies, Chet.

Chet   Don't worry, Adi. You'll be fine.

Adi   But poor old Killer is a bit
battered from all the whacks
he's had.

Chet   Hmmm. But he's only got to last
for one more hit.

Adi   Yes, but what if Billy spots we've switched his conker?

Chet   Then you're in deep doo-doo.

Adi   Cheers, Chet. That makes me feel so much better.

Billy Basher struts out to face Adi. He holds up his conker and dangles it in front of Adi.

Billy   (sneering) Okay, kid. Take your best shot.

Adi   Ref, will you come in really close?
           I want you to be sure Billy
           doesn't move his conker
           when I try to hit it.

Billy Yeah, you do that, Ref. I don't
           want anyone saying Billy Basher
           is a cheat.

The ref puts his head level with
the conker. Then Adi draws 'Killer' back
on its string. He tries to take aim,
but his hand is shaking like a jelly
in a high wind.

Chet   Come on, Adi. Let him have it.

Adi   But my hand won't keep still.

Billy and the ref wink at each other.
They both think the cash is as good
as theirs. This makes Adi mad.
His hand stops shaking and he swings
his conker down hard.

It smacks into the fake conker –
which explodes! Stinky stuff splashes
all over Billy and the ref.

Chet   Nice one, Adi!

Adi   Oh dear. It looks like your
conker was rotten, Billy.
And now you smell worse
than a skunk wearing
a mucky nappy!

Billy   Grrrr!

Chet   Yay! Adi is the new conker king!

The crowd cheers and claps. Adi punches
the air. Billy and the ref slink away.
They pong too much to stay. Adi gets
the conker crown and the cash prize.

Chet   Well done, Adi. Billy Basher
             won't forget that final in a hurry.

Adi   Too right. It was a real stinker –
             for him!

About the author

Roger Hurn has:

- had a hit record in Turkey
- won *The Weakest Link* on TV
- swum with sharks on the Great Barrier Reef.

Now he's a writer, and he hopes you like reading about the Mystery Mob as much as he likes writing about them.

Conker Quiz

Questions

1 Why can't you play conkers in the jungle?

2 Why does Tarzan spend so much time playing conkers?

3 What do you do if you see an elephant coming at you with a conker on the end of its trunk?

4 What do you do if you're playing conkers with a bad-tempered gorilla?

5 Why was the conker disqualified for wearing a ballet dress?

6 How do you stay cool when playing conkers?

7 What do you call a conker when it's lost a game?

8 What do a conker and a man who does dangerous stunts have in common?

40

Answers

1 Because there are too many cheetahs.
2 Because he's trying to practise his swing.
3 Get out of its way!
4 Let it win.
5 Because it was tu-tu hard!
6 Stand next to your fans.
7 Conkered.
8 They're both nuts.

How did you score?

✋ If you got all eight conker answers correct, then you are all-conkering!

✋ If you got six conker answers correct, then there's nothing nutty about you.

✋ If you got fewer than four conker answers correct, then you have conked out big time.

When I was a kid

Question When you were a kid, did you ever play conkers?

Roger Yes, I was a conker nut!

Question Did you ever win?

Roger Yes. I was so good that my mates called me Roger the Conker-er.

Question Doh! So you think playing conkers is good?

Roger Yes. You can learn loads from playing conkers.

Question What do you mean?

Roger Well, a conker once hit me on the head.

Question So what did you learn from that?

Roger I learnt not to stand underneath horse chestnut trees in the conker season.

Adi's favourite conker joke

Which famous nut invaded England in 1066?

William the Conker-er!

How to win at conkers

You need to choose a very dense conker. You do this by putting them in a bucket of water and seeing if they sink – not by asking them really hard questions and picking the one that gets the most wrong.

Get an adult to bore a hole through the middle of your conker. They do this with a sharp skewer – not by telling the conker all about their favourite hobby.

Thread a bootlace through the hole, and tie a knot at one end, so that it doesn't pull through. If you've used the lace from your Dad's football boots, be careful he doesn't give you the boot when he finds out!

Make sure you can wrap the lace twice around your clenched hand and still have 20 centimetres between your hand and the conker. When you swing the lace make sure it's not so long that the conker hits you on your conk!

You can toughen up your conker by covering it in nail varnish. Some people say this is against the rules. But if you do decide to do it anyway, don't use that bright red sparkly stuff – it's a dead giveaway!

Five fantastic facts about conkers

1 Conkers are the nuts of the horse chestnut tree. They used to be fed to horses to make their coats shine. That's why they're called 'horse' chestnuts.

2 The first recorded game of conkers took place in 1848. Before that the game was usually played with snail shells.

3 TV star Michael Palin was once disqualified from the World Conker Championships for soaking his conker in vinegar and baking it!

4 Some people think that spiders will not come into a room that has conkers in it. Why not try it out and see if they're right? (You mustn't hit the spider with the conker – it's the smell the spider doesn't like!)

5 The world record-holding conker is a 5000er – which means it has beaten 5000 other conkers. Now that's what I call an all-conkering conker!

Conker lingo

Belt A way of hitting the conker – not the thing that stops your trousers from falling down.

Nut The proper name for a conker – not a very silly person.

Stamps If your opponent drops his conker, or you knock it out of his hand, you can shout 'stamps' and jump on it. But don't shout 'stamps' in a post office. If you do you'll have to buy some.

No stamps This is what you shout if you drop your conker – not what you say when your mum asks you why you haven't written a thank-you letter to your Gran.

Striker The person who's aiming the conker ready for a hit – not the overpaid bloke who plays up front for your favourite football team.

Mystery Mob

Mystery Mob Set 1:

Mystery Mob and the Abominable Snowman
Mystery Mob and the Big Match
Mystery Mob and the Circus of Doom
Mystery Mob and the Creepy Castle
Mystery Mob and the Haunted Attic
Mystery Mob and the Hidden Treasure
Mystery Mob and the Magic Bottle
Mystery Mob and the Missing Millions
Mystery Mob and the Monster on the Moor
Mystery Mob and the Mummy's Curse
Mystery Mob and the Time Machine
Mystery Mob and the UFO

Mystery Mob Set 2:

Mystery Mob and the Ghost Town
Mystery Mob and the Bonfire Night Plot
Mystery Mob and the April Fools' Day Joker
Mystery Mob and the Great Pancake Day Race
Mystery Mob and the Scary Santa
Mystery Mob and the Conker Conspiracy
Mystery Mob and the Top Talent Contest
Mystery Mob and the Night in the Waxworks
Mystery Mob and the Runaway Train
Mystery Mob and the Wrong Robot
Mystery Mob and the Day of the Dinosaurs
Mystery Mob and the Man-eating Tiger

RISING ★ STARS

Mystery Mob books are available from most booksellers.

**For mail order information
please call Rising Stars on 0871 47 23 010
or visit www.risingstars-uk.com**